TO TINE

FROM MOR

SUMMER 1966.

The FIRST BOOK of SHORT VERSE

FRANKLIN WATTS, INC. 575 Lexington Avenue, New York 22

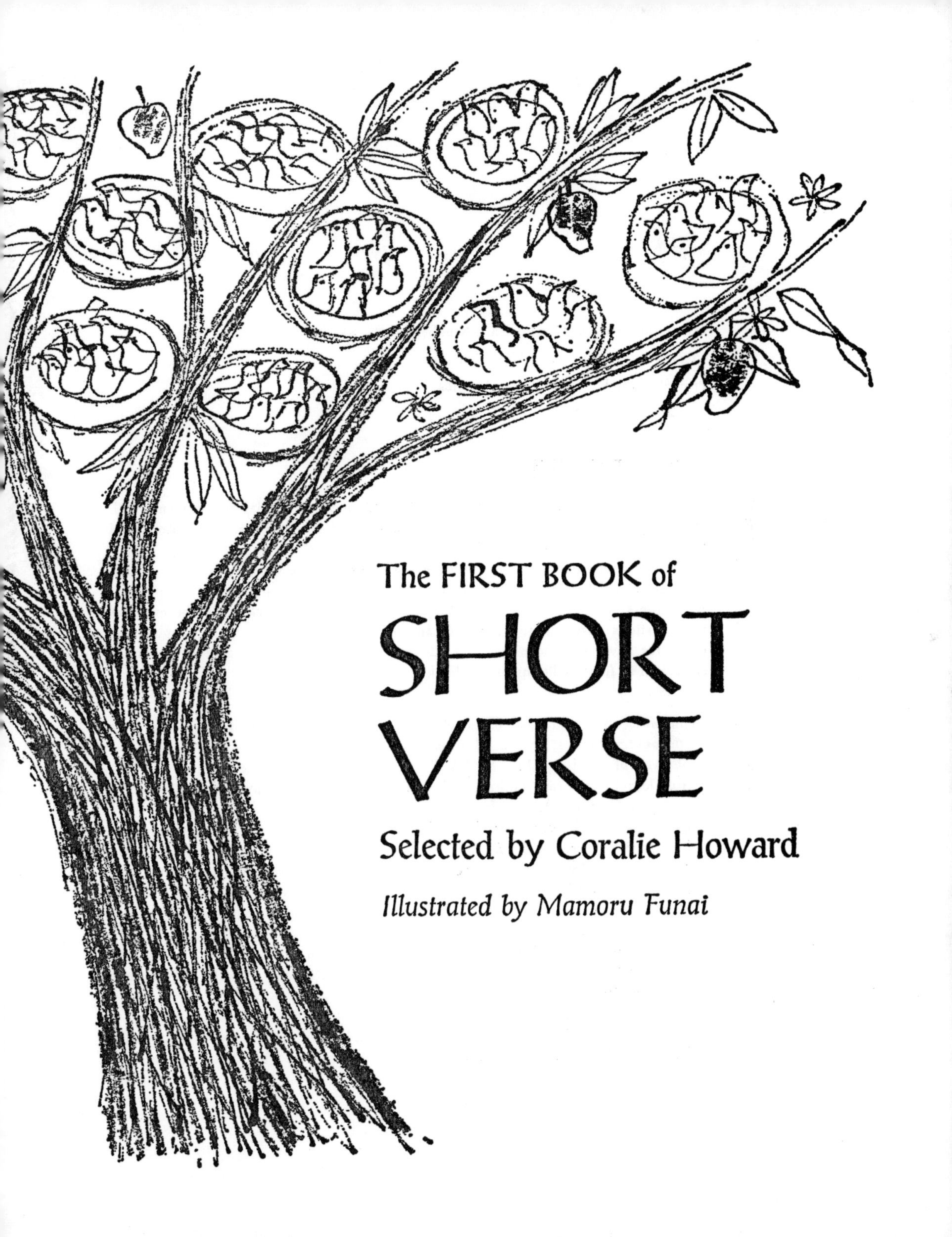

The FIRST BOOK of

SHORT VERSE

Selected by Coralie Howard

Illustrated by Mamoru Funai

Library of Congress Catalog Card Number: 64–17783

Printed in the United States of America
2 3 4 5

ACKNOWLEDGMENTS

The selections in this book are used by permission and special arrangements with the proprietors of their respective copyrights who are listed below. The editor's and publisher's thanks to all who made this collection possible.

The editor and publisher have made every effort to trace the ownership of all material contained herein. It is their belief that the necessary permissions from publishers, authors, and authorized agents have been obtained in all cases. In the event of any questions arising as to the use of any material, the editor and publisher express regret for any error unconsciously made and will be pleased to make the necessary correction in future editions of this book.

Appleton-Century and Basil Blackwell for "Robin's Song," by E. L. M. King, from *50 Country Rhymes*, by E. L. M. King.

Bobbs-Merrill Company, Inc., for "A Wee Little Worm," by James Whitcomb Riley, from *Joyful Poems for Children*, by James Whitcomb Riley. Copyright © 1946, 1960, by Bobbs-Merrill Company, Inc.

Book House for Children, The, for "African Lullaby," trans. by Holling C. Holling, from *In the Nursery of My Book House*, by Olive Beaupré Miller, copyright © 1960; "Mount Fuji," by Onitsura, "The Rag Picker," by Ransetsu, and "Lightning," unknown, from *Little Pictures of Japan*, by Olive Beaupré Miller, copyright © 1950.

Cambridge University Press, for "Cleis," trans. by J. M. Edmonds, from *Some Greek Poems of Love and Beauty*, by J. M. Edmonds.

Clarendon Press, The, for "Golden Fish," by Titanomachia, trans. by T. F. Higham, and "The Poet's Shield," by Archilochus, trans. by Sir W. Morris, from the *Oxford Book of Greek Verse in Translation*.

Harold A. Conrad, for "High Noon, Manhattan," by Ralph Cohn.

Thomas Y. Crowell Company, for "I've Got a Dog," "The Mule," "My Love for You," from *A Diller, A Dollar*, by Lillian Morrison, copyright 1955 by Lillian Morrison.

Curtis Brown, Ltd. and Ogden Nash, for "The Hunter," by Ogden Nash, from *Verses*, by Ogden Nash, copyright © 1947, by Ogden Nash.

Doubleday & Company, Inc., for "Child on Top of a Greenhouse," by Theodore Roethke, from *Words for the Wind*, by Theodore Roethke, copyright © 1946 by Editorial Publications, Inc.

Doubleday & Company, Inc., for "Singing-Time," by Rose Fyleman, from *The Fairy Green*, by Rose Fyleman, copyright 1923 by George H. Doran Company.

Doubleday & Company, Inc. and Harold G. Henderson, for "The Cat," by Issa, "Cherry Blossoms," "On the Road to Nara," and "The End of Summer," by Basho, "The Tree Frog," by Kikaku, "The Scarecrow," by Boncho, "The Barley Field," by Sora, "Onitsura's First Poem," "The Little Valley in Spring," "Coolness," and "The World Upside Down," by Onitsura, "In the Paddy Field," by Raizan, "Spring Rains," by Buson, "Conscience," by Issa, "The Parasol," by Seiho, and "Sounds," by Wafu, from *An Introduction to Haiku*, by Harold G. Henderson, copyright © 1958 by Harold G. Henderson.

Doubleday & Company, Inc., for "City Nights," by James Flexner, "December," by Sanderson Vanderbilt, "Morning," by Nathalie Swan, from *In Creative Youth*, by Hughes Mearns, copyright © 1925 by Doubleday & Company, Inc.; "The Honey-bee," by Don Marquis, from "Certain Maxims of Archy," from *Archy and Mehitabel*, by Don Marquis. Copyright © 1927 by Doubleday & Company, Inc.

E. P. Dutton & Company, Inc., for "Of Courtesy," and "Of Quarrels," by Arthur Guiterman, from *A Poet's Proverbs*, by Arthur Guiterman, copyright 1924 by E. P. Dutton & Company, Inc., renewed, 1952, by Mrs. Vida L. Guiterman.

Faber & Faber, Ltd., for "Song for a Dance," by Francis Beaumont, from the *Faber Book of Children's Verse*, ed. by Janet Adam Smith.

Harcourt, Brace & World, Inc., for "Sea Wash," "Buffalo Dusk," "Pods," and "Slippery," by Carl Sandburg, from *Smoke and Steel*, by Carl Sandburg, copyright © 1920 by Harcourt, Brace & World, Inc., renewed, 1948, by Carl Sandburg; "Primer Lesson," by Carl Sandburg, from *Slabs of the Sunburnt West*, by Carl Sandburg, copyright © 1922, by Harcourt, Brace & World, Inc., renewed, 1950, by Carl Sandburg; "Grassroots," "Cricket March," and "Splinter," by Carl Sandburg, from *Good Morning, America*, by Carl Sandburg, copyright 1928, © 1956 by Carl Sandburg.

Harper & Row, Inc., for "The Unknown Color," by Countee Cullen, from *Copper Sun*, by Countee Cullen, copyright 1927 by Harper & Brothers, renewed, 1955, by Ida M. Cullen.

Highlights for Children, Inc., for "Mountains," by Susan Roberts, from the March, 1962 issue of *Highlights for Children*, copyright © 1962.

Holt, Rinehart & Winston, Inc., for "Lodged," and "Fireflies in the Garden," by Robert Frost, from *Complete Poems of Robert Frost*, copyright 1916, 1921, 1928 by Holt, Rinehart & Winston, Inc. Copyright renewed 1944, © 1956 by Robert Frost; "Span of Life," and "Hardship of Accounting," by Robert Frost, from *Complete Poems of Robert Frost*, copyright 1936 by Robert Frost, renewed © 1964 by Lesley Frost Ballantine.

Holt, Rinehart & Winston, Inc., for "Valentine Greetings," by Kathryn L. Sexton, "Surgeon's Hands," by Don Russell, "Song," by June Nakagiri, "Love," by Frederico Velasquez, "Summer Wind," by Barbara Johnson, and "Traders," by David Howard, from *Let Them Write Poetry*, by Nina Willis Walter.

Houghton Mifflin Company, for "White Season," and "Blue Smoke," by Frances Frost, from *Pool in the Meadow*, by Frances Frost.

William Hurley, for "Haiku," by Debby Innes, "Cinquain," by Kathleen Vogt, "Haiku," by Devra Jeffers, "The Sun," by Jodelle Hulse, "Haiku," by Dick Sanders.

Jonathan Cape Ltd. and the Executors of the R. A. Furness Estate, for "Under a Laurel," by Anyte, trans. by R. A. Furness, from *Translations from the Greek Anthology*, by R. A. Furness.

Alfred A. Knopf, Inc., for "Tanka," trans. by Eunice Tietjens, reprinted from *Poetry of the Orient*, by Eunice Tietjens, copyright 1928 by Alfred A. Knopf, Inc., renewed, 1956, by Cloyd Head; "The Elephant," by Hilaire Belloc, reprinted from *Cautionary Verses*, by Hilaire Belloc, published 1941 by Alfred A. Knopf, Inc.; "The Grand Canyon," by Adelaide Crapsey, reprinted from *Verse*, by Adelaide Crapsey, published 1941 by Alfred A. Knopf, Inc.; "Mexican Market Woman," by Langston Hughes, reprinted from *The Dream Keeper*, by Langston Hughes, copyright 1926 by Alfred A. Knopf, Inc., renewed, 1954, by Langston Hughes; "Snail," by Langston Hughes, reprinted from *Fields of Wonder*, by Langston Hughes, copyright 1947 by Langston Hughes.

Alfred A. Knopf, Inc., for "On Seeing Weatherbeaten Trees," by Adelaide Crapsey, from *Verse*, by Adelaide Crapsey; for "13 Ways of Looking at a Blackbird," by Wallace Stevens, from *The Collected Poems of Wallace Stevens*.

J. B. Lippincott Company, for "Song," "Water," and "Dandelion," by Hilda Conkling, from *Poems by a Little Girl*, by Hilda Conkling, copyright 1920, 1947 by Hilda Conkling; "Blow the Stars Home," by Eleanor Farjeon, from *Poems for Children*, by Eleanor Farjeon, copyright 1926, 1954 by Eleanor Farjeon; "The Purple Cow," "I Wish That My Room Had a Floor," and "On Digital Extremities," by Gelette Burgess, from *Burgess Nonsense Book*, by Gelette Burgess.

Little, Brown & Company and J. M. Dent & Sons, Ltd., for "The Camel," and "The Octopus," by Ogden Nash, from *Verses From 1929*, by Ogden Nash, copyright 1933 by The Curtis Publishing Company, copyright 1942 by Ogden Nash.

Macmillan Company, The, for "March," and "Old Stones," by Elizabeth Coatsworth, from *Summer Green*, by Elizabeth Coatsworth, copyright © 1948 by The Macmillan Company; "Washed in Silver," by James Stephens, from *Collected Poems*, by James Stephens, copyright © 1915 by The Macmillan Company, renewed, 1943, by James Stephens; "The Dark Hills," by E. A. Robinson, from *The Collected Poems of Edwin Arlington Robinson*, by E. A. Robinson, copyright © 1920 by The Macmillan Company, renewed, 1948, by Ruth Nivison.

Virgil Markham, for "Duty," by Edwin Markham.

Alfred H. Marks, for "The Octopus," by Basho.

Mabel Mountsier, for "Drowsyheads," by Gertrude Louise Cheney, "By the Fire," by Julia Jane White, "Spring," group, "Popcorn," by Edith S. Campbell, and "The Way of the River," by William Kimball Flaccus, from *Singing Youth*, ed. by Mabel Mountsier.

New Directions, for "Poem," by William Carlos Williams, from *The Selected Poems of William Carlos Williams*, © 1949, by William Carlos Williams.

Oxford University Press, for "Cattle," by Banko, "Foxes Playing," by Buson, "Baby's Hands," by Gomi, and "My Little Sword-Bearer," by Shigen, from *A Year of Japanese Epigrams*, by William N. Porter.

Robert Payne, for "The Summit Temple," by Li Po, from *The White Pony*, by Robert Payne, published by John Day Company.

Peter Pauper Press, The, for "The Heron," by Zuiryu, "The First Firefly," by Issa, "My Hut," by Issa, "The Kite," by Kubonta, "Icicles," by Onitsura, "The Wild Geese," by Roka, "Frogs," by Wakyu and "The Sparrow," by Shiki, from *The Four Seasons*.

A. D. Peters & Company, for "A Maltese Dog," by Tymnes, trans. by Edmund Blunden; "Washerwoman's Song," by L. A. G. Strong, from *Dublin Days*, by L. A. G. Strong; "The Early Morning," by Hilaire Belloc, from *Sonnets and Verse*, by Hilaire Belloc.

Viking Press, Inc., The, for "Firefly," by Elizabeth Madox Roberts, from *Under the Tree*, by Elizabeth Madox Roberts, copyright 1922 by B. W. Heubsch, Inc., © 1959 by Ivor S. Roberts.

Webster Publishing Division of McGraw-Hill Book Company, Inc., for "Icebergs," by Estelle Rooks, "City Dawn," by Naomi Robin, "Vagabondia," by Gertrude Buckman, "A Lover to His Doubting Lady," by J. J., and "Philosophical Poem," unknown.

Woman's Day Magazine, for "Haiku," by Roger Pearson, and "Haiku," by Deborah Basnett.

Contents

VIII

Wisdom

Why People Write Poetry

Let us suppose that you have visited the ocean. You saw, heard, felt, smelled, and even tasted the ocean. The day was fair or stormy, warm or wintry. Perhaps you swam; perhaps you gathered shells or creatures on shore. Maybe you were lonely that day; maybe you were unusually happy. However you felt, your experience of the ocean was special because you experienced it with your own senses and emotions.

How could you give your experience of the ocean to someone who had never been near it? One way you could do this would be to write a poem about it. As a painter uses colors, and a musician musical tones, a poet uses words to express his feelings about life. He tries to create a pattern of words that will make the reader see what he saw, and feel what he felt.

Words arranged in certain kinds of patterns we call verse. When verse makes us feel deeply, we call it poetry. Poetry may be written about anything that is important to the poet: a moment of beauty; loneliness; anger at injustice; reverence; even something ugly or unpleasant, if the poet draws meaning from it.

The poetry and verse in this book have many different moods, subjects, and styles because they are by many different poets. Some are several thousand years old; some are by modern schoolchildren; some are by famous poets; some are by unknown people. They come from many centuries, countries, and conditions of life. But the poetry still speaks to us, because it was truly felt.

Although these poems are short, they often express so much in a few lines that you will want to read them again and again. The poet uses his imagination and the reader must also use his imagination to rediscover the poet's meaning. Someone once said, "We are all poets when we read poetry."

We are all poets, too, when we use our senses and imaginations to explore the world for ourselves. To learn more about the ways that poets preserve and communicate their feelings and experiences, read the section called WRITING POETRY at the back of this book. If you are not already a student poet, it may help you to begin expressing your own experiences in poetry.

CORALIE HOWARD

The FIRST BOOK of SHORT VERSE

I

Familiar Things

Good poetry helps us to see the world around us with new eyes. As the writers of these short verses describe such commonplace things as the early morning hours, summer gardens, animals, wind, and clouds, do they help you to look at the world as though you had never seen it before? What do these poems tell you about the people who wrote them?

THE EARLY MORNING

Hilaire Belloc

The moon on the one hand, the dawn on the other:
The moon is my sister, the dawn is my brother.
The moon on my left and the dawn on my right.
My brother, good morning: my sister, good night.

BLOW THE STARS HOME

Eleanor Farjeon

Blow the stars home, Wind,
  blow the stars home
Ere morning drowns them
  in a golden foam.

MORNING

Nathalie Swan, grade 7

Twigs crackle frostily in the cold blue light of morning;
Hazy smoke from kitchen fires while light is dawning;
Mountain peaks are misty in the yellow morning sun,
And many a dog is barking that the day's work is begun.

CITY DAWN

Naomi Rogin, high school

A gay morning breeze
  Danced to the rattling music
    Of the milk bottles.

The dawn in this Persian poet's native land was sudden and dramatic. Who—or what—is the Hunter of the East?

From the RUBÁIYÁT

Omar Khayyám

Awake! for Morning in the Bowl of Night
Has flung the Stone that puts the Stars to Flight:
  And Lo! the Hunter of the East has caught
The Sultan's Turret in a Noose of Light.

COLD, FROSTY MORNING

Unknown.

Cold, frosty morning,
Ground all covered with snow,
Got no shoes to put on my feet,
Frost gwine to bite my toe.

NOONDAY

Lyman Furness

Birds are silent,
Locusts shrill;
Light lies sleeping
On the hill.

AFTERNOONS

Unknown English Poet

Prodigal summer afternoons
Buzz and shrill, shimmering bright;
Brooding afternoons in winter
Muffle sound and hoard the light.

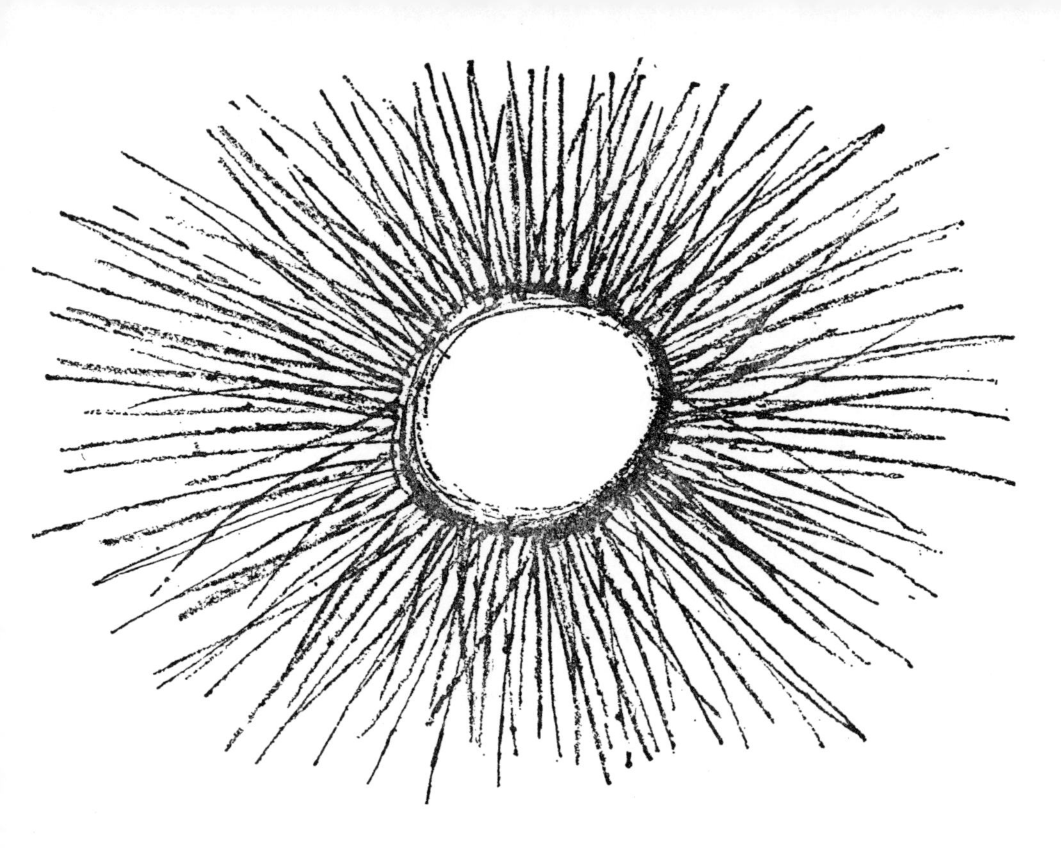

THE DARK HILLS

Edwin Arlington Robinson

❦

Dark hills at evening in the west,
Where sunset hovers like a sound
Of golden horns that sang to rest
Old bones of warriors under ground,
Far now from all the bannered ways
Where flash the legions of the sun,
You fade—as if the last of days
Were fading, and all wars were done.

THE MOON

Louise Garnett

See how the sky
Is sailing its kite,
Trailing a hundred stars
Over the night.

WASHED IN SILVER

James Stephens

Gleaming in silver are the hills!
Blazing in silver is the sea!
And a silvery radiance spills
Where the moon drives royally!
Clad in silver tissue, I
March magnificently by!

In "free verse" the poet divides his lines according to the natural pauses in his thought, and does not concern himself with rhyme.

THE SUMMIT TEMPLE

Li-Po TRANSLATED BY ROBERT PAYNE

Here it is night: I stay at the Summit Temple.
Here I can touch the stars with my hand.
I dare not speak aloud in the silence
For fear of disturbing the dwellers of Heaven.

DROWSYHEAD AT NIGHT

Gertrude Louise Cheney, age 5

I'm tired—
Tired as the lazy stones
That are always sitting down,
Most tired as the sky
That stays up all night and day
Whether it's early with spider-vines
Or late with frogs singing.

NIGHT BY THE FIRE

Julia Jane White, age 6

I like to sit by the fireside,
It is so pretty and light at eventide.
I read my stories while mother listens;
The bright coal snaps, sparkles, and glistens.
Sometimes we have an apple or two—
There is just nothing I'd rather do.

CITY NIGHTS

James Flexner, grade 8

When the lights of the city are bright and they gleam,
And the moon looks down on the level street,
I always dream the selfsame dream:
Of hills that are wide and of woods that are green
And of places where two brooks meet.

SPRING

Composed by a group of six-year-old children

Spring is the time of flowers,
The time of green things growing,
Meadows of velvety green grass,
Trees and shrubs a soft yellow-green,
Like the feathers of a wild canary.

MARCH

Elizabeth Coatsworth

A blue day,
a blue jay
and a good beginning.
One crow,
melting snow—
spring's winning!

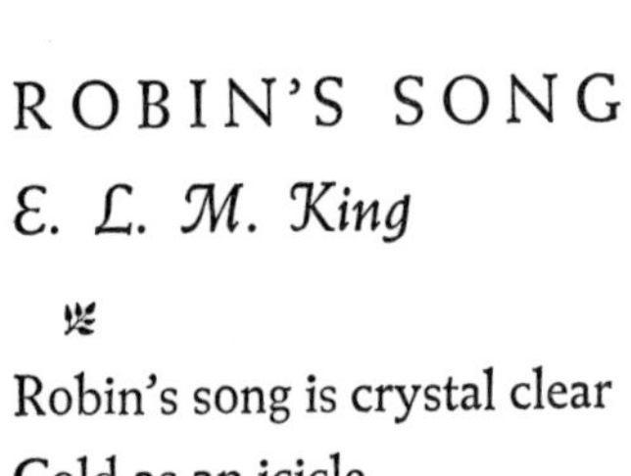

ROBIN'S SONG

E. L. M. King

Robin's song is crystal clear
Cold as an icicle,
Sharp as a spear.
I have seen Spring lift her head,
Snowdrops a-shivering,
Winter is dead.

GROW AND GROW

Kari Granda, age 7

Spring! Spring! Spring at last.
Raindrops make the flowers grow.
The warm wind makes all trees glow
It's nice to feel the warm wind blow,
and as it blows,
I grow and grow.

KITE DAYS

Mark Sawyer

A kite, a sky, and a good firm breeze,
And acres of ground away from trees,
And one hundred yards of clean, strong string—
Oh boy, Oh boy! I call that spring!

The Japanese have a very old verse form called tanka.
A tanka *is a little poem consisting of only five lines.*

TANKA

Unknown TRANSLATED BY EUNICE TIETJENS

Blossoms of the plum
Gleam through fallen snow today.
Better let them stand!
I had gathered some for you—
But they melted in my hand.

UNDER A LAUREL

Anyte TRANSLATED BY R. A. FURNESS

Sit all beneath fair leaves of spreading bay,
And draw sweet water from a timely spring,
And let your breathless limbs, this summer day,
Rest, in the west wind's airy buffeting.

RUSHES IN A WATERY PLACE

Christina Rossetti

Rushes in a watery place,
   And reeds in a hollow;
A soaring skylark in the sky,
   A darting swallow;
And where pale blossom used to hang
   Ripe fruit to follow.

CRICKET MARCH

Carl Sandburg

As the corn becomes higher
The one shrill of a summer cricket
Becomes two and ten
With a shrilling surer than last month.

As the banners of the corn
Come to their highest flying in the wind,
The summer crickets come to a marching army.

IN THE LANE

Madison Cawein

When the hornet hangs in the hollyhock,
And the brown bee drones i' the rose,
And the west is a red-streaked four-o'clock,
And the summer is near its close—
It's oh, for the gate and the locust lane
And dusk and dew and home again.

FROST SHALL FREEZE

Eighth-century Anglo-Saxon poet. Unknown.

Frost shall freeze; fire melt wood;
Earth shall blossom; ice shall bridge,
Shall roof the waters, wondrously lock
Earth's budding growth. But One shall unbind
The fetters of frost, the Almighty God.
Winter shall pass, fair weather return,
The sun-hot summer, the restless sea.

SILENCE IN CAMP

Sioux Indian children

Today is cold;
The snow is falling.
The only noise
Is a pheasant calling.

BLUE SMOKE

Frances Frost

Beside the mountain roads, the men
Heap and burn the leaves again.
While the mountain dusks grow brief and cold,
The children scuffle through fallen gold,
Knowing that soon, some early dawn,
The peaks will be white and the leaves be gone.

ICEBERGS

Estelle Rooks, high-school student

Winter,
Greedy Midas,
Has touched the laughing waves
And transformed them into frozen
Silver.

BEGGAR'S RHYME

Unknown English poet

Christmas is coming, the geese are getting fat,
Please to put a penny in the old man's hat;
If you haven't got a penny, a ha'penny will do,
If you haven't got a ha'penny, God bless you.

DECEMBER

Sanderson Vanderbilt, high-school student

A little boy stood on the corner
And shoveled bits of dirty, soggy snow
Into the sewer—
With a jagged piece of tin.

He was helping spring come.

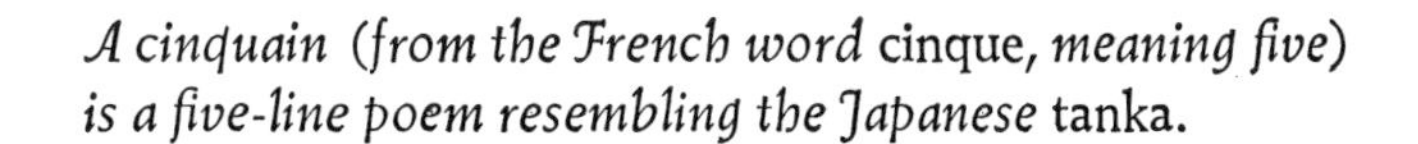

A cinquain (from the French word cinque, *meaning five) is a five-line poem resembling the Japanese* tanka.

THE GRAND CANYON (Cinquain)

Adelaide Crapsey

By Zeus!
Shout word of this
To the eldest dead! Titans,
Gods, Heroes, come who have once more
A home!

MOUNTAINS

Susan Roberts, age 9

Oh, the mountains with their
 blueberry-sherbet bottoms
And their whipped-cream tops:
They look like a bowl of ice cream
In a grass dish.

THE WIND

Unknown

Arthur O'Bower has broken his bands,
And he's come roaring owre the lands;
The King o' Scots and a' his power
Canna turn Arthur O'Bower.

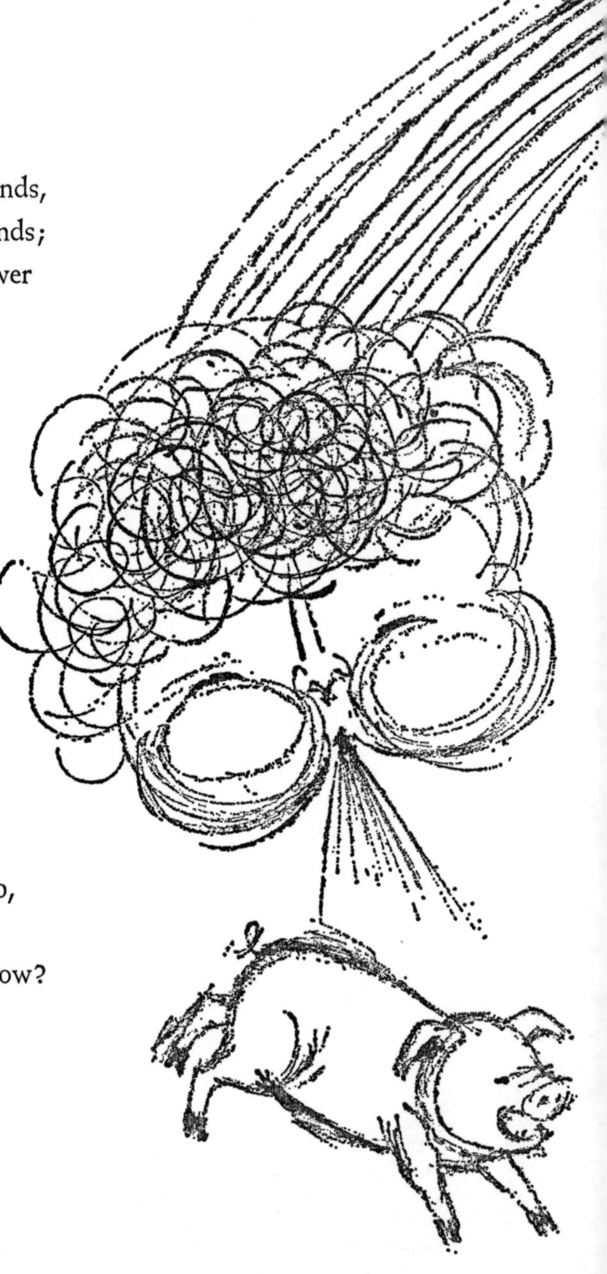

O WIND

Christina Rossetti

O wind, why do you never rest,
Wandering, whistling to and fro,
Bringing rain out of the west,
From the dim north bringing snow?

In an old Irish myth there were said to be twelve winds, each of a different color. The idea for this poem must have come from an old country belief that pigs can see the wind.

THE UNKNOWN COLOR

Countee Cullen

I've often heard my mother say,
When great winds blew across the day,
And cuddled close and out of sight,
The young pigs squealed with sudden fright
Like something speared or javelined,
"Poor little pigs, they see the wind."

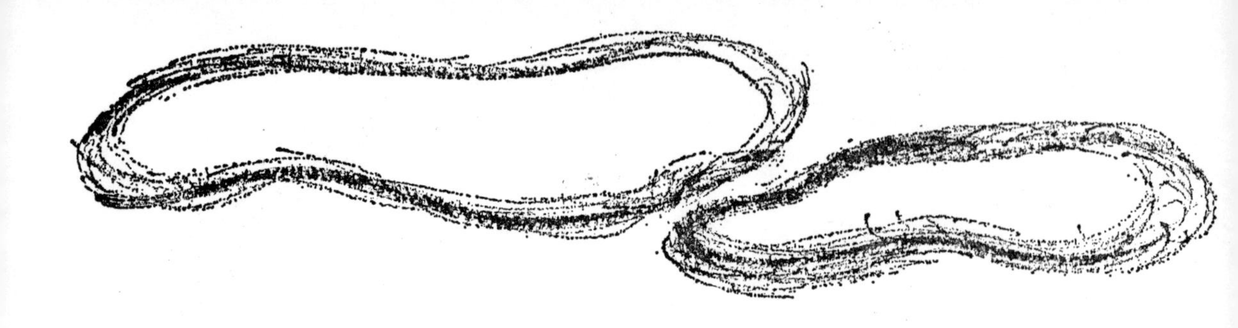

WASHERWOMAN'S SONG

L. A. G. Strong

Clouds, clouds, clouds in the sky,
The heavenly washing is hung out to dry!
Billowing, bellying, full in the breeze,
Leaping and tugging as gay as you please.
Look, children, look at 'em! If they was mine,
I'd be in dread that they'd blow off the line.

CHILD ON TOP OF A GREENHOUSE

Theodore Roethke

The wind billowing out the seat of my britches,
My feet crackling splinters of glass and dried putty,
The half-grown chrysanthemums staring up like accusers,
Up through the streaked glass, flashing with sunlight,
A few white clouds all rushing eastward,
A line of elms plunging and tossing like horses,
And everyone, everyone, pointing up and shouting!

CLOUDS

Ricky Rieden, grade 6

Swirling,
Whipping around,
Floating into tall mountains,
Imprisoned by the howling wind,
Drifting.

A FIRE

Donald E., elementary school

First a flicker, then a spark,
And a crackling of twigs,
Then as it fades from the sky
The ashes
That are left
Seem like a million unlit stars.

THE WAY OF THE RIVER

William Flaccus, age 12

Down through the forest, dodging the rocks,
Now rushing, now roaring,
In cataracts pouring,
I pass by the home of the beaver and fox.
Walls have I chiseled and rocks have I filed.
I follow my way—the Way of the Wild.

WATER

Hilda Conkling, age 6

The world turns softly
Not to spill its lakes and rivers.
The water is held in its arms
And the sky is held in the water.
What is water,
That pours silver,
And can hold the sky?

SEA WASH

Carl Sandburg

The sea wash never ends.
The sea wash repeats, repeats.
Only old songs? Is that all the sea knows?
  Only the old strong songs?
  Is that all?
The sea wash repeats, repeats.

TRADERS

David Howard, age 9

The earth and sea are traders:
The sea brings sand to the earth
And the earth gives its tumbling, roaring rivers
To the sea.

HIGH NOON, MANHATTAN

Ralph Cohn

The steel-jacketed towers
Open, spilling forth
The stenographers in their fluttering scarves.

PODS

Carl Sandburg

Pea pods cling to stems.
Neponset, the village,
Clings to the Burlington railway main line.
Terrible midnight limiteds roar through
Hauling sleepers to the Rockies and Sierras.
The earth is slightly shaken
And Neponset trembles slightly in its sleep.

BOBBYPIN SONG

A four-year-old sang this as she played with a bobbypin

My name is Peter Bobbypin—
  Poing, poing.
I only got two legs,
That's all there is of me;
My name is Peter Bobbypin—
  Poing, poing.

SURGEON'S HANDS

Don Russell, age 12

His hands are swift,
His hands are sure;
He has the gift
To heal and cure.

THE RUNNER

Walt Whitman

On a flat road runs the well-trained runner
He is lean and sinewy with muscular legs,
He is thinly clothed, he leans forward as he runs,
With lightly closed fists and arms partially raised.

POPCORN

Edith Campbell, age 11

Hopping up and down the cage,
Popping all about,
Bursting into fluff with rage,
Striving to get out.

These young poets not only looked at things; they listened to them, too. Ears are as important as eyes.

RAIN

Scott Phillips, grade 1

Rain sounds like my little dog's feet
  on the kitchen floor.

SONG

June Nakagiri, age 6

A little bird
Hopped on my window.
His song
Got into my dream.

WHITE SEASON

Frances Frost

In the winter the rabbits match their pelts to the earth.
With ears laid back, they go
Blown through the silver hollow, the silver thicket,
Like puffs of snow.

LOCUST SONG

Zuni Indian

Locust, locust, playing a flute,
Locust, locust, playing a flute!
    Away up above on the pine-tree bough,
        Closely clinging,
                Playing a flute,
                Playing a flute!

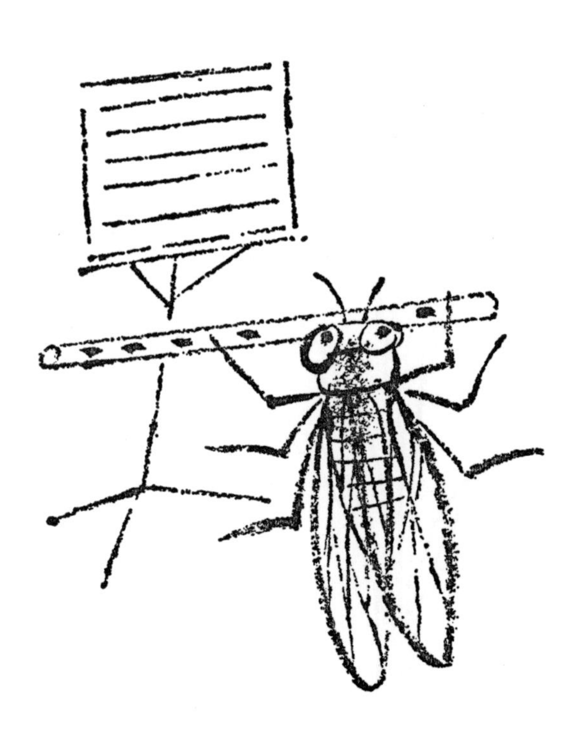

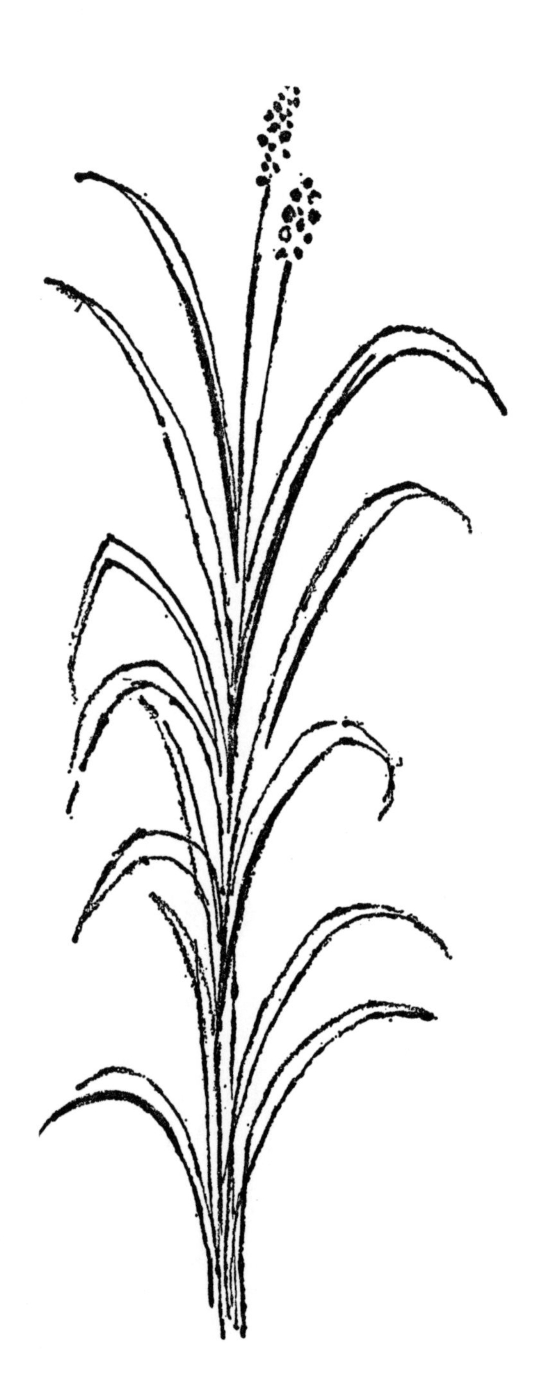

CINQUAIN

Kathleen Vogt, grade 7

There was
A horse trotting
That had a clip-clop beat
That lingers like a song upon
My mind.

THE HORSE

Robin Niswander, grade 3

The horse with long-lashed eyes,
Both sad and wise,
Looked at me intently.
His face was smooth and soft,
He let me stroke it gently.

FIREFLY

Elizabeth Maddox Roberts

A little light is going by,
Is going up to see the sky,
A little light with wings.
I never could have thought of it,
To have a little bug all lit
And made to go on wings.

SNAIL

Langston Hughes

Little snail,
Dreaming you go.
Weather and rose
Is all you know.

Weather and rose
Is all you see,
Drinking
The dewdrop's
Mystery.

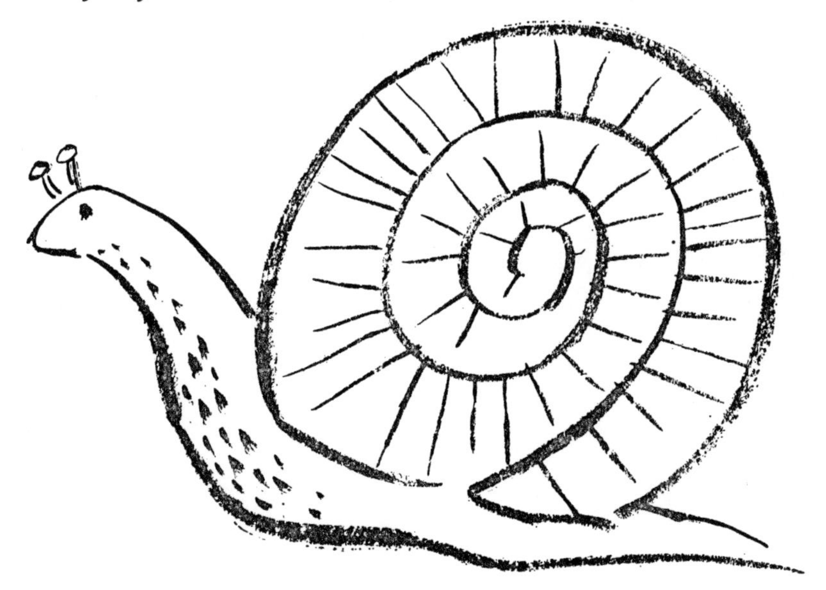

KA-NI-GA SONG

American Indian TRANSLATED BY JAMES POWELL

The poor little bee
That lives in the tree
The poor little bee
That lives in the tree
Has only one arrow
In his quiver.

A nursery school child made up this poem.
What impressed him most about the squirrel?

A LITTLE SQUIRREL

I saw a little squirrel,
Sitting in a tree;
He was eating a nut
And wouldn't look at me.

From THIRTEEN WAYS OF LOOKING AT A BLACKBIRD

Wallace Stevens

I

Among twenty snowy mountains
The only moving thing
Was the eye of the blackbird.

II

I was of three minds
Like a tree
In which there are three blackbirds.

XIII

It was evening all afternoon.
It was snowing
And it was going to snow.
The blackbird sat
In the cedar limbs.

GOLDEN FISH

Titanomachia TRANSLATED BY T. F. HIGHAM

Mute fishes, too, with eyes of gold inlaid,
Through paradisal water swam and played.

SLIPPERY

Carl Sandburg

❧

The six-month child
Fresh from the tub
Wriggles in our hands.
This is our fish child.
Give her a nickname: Slippery.

ENVOI

Algernon Charles Swinburne

❧

Fly, white butterflies, out to sea,
Frail pale wings for the wind to try,
Small white wings that we scarce can see,
Fly.

Some fly light as a laugh of glee,
Some fly soft as a low long sigh:
All to the haven where each should be,
Fly.

William Carlos Williams was not only a poet, but also a doctor, trained in careful observation. Do you see what the cat is doing in this poem? Do the short lines help suggest the cat's motions?

POEM

William Carlos Williams

As the cat
climbed over
the top of

the jamcloset
first the right
forefoot

carefully
then the hind
stepped down

into the pit of
the empty
flowerpot.

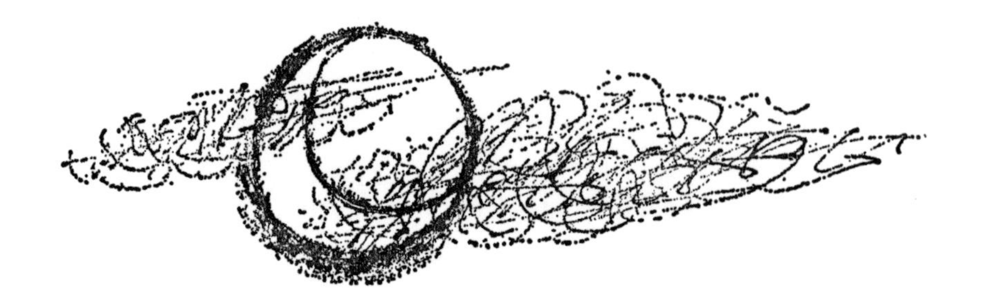

II

Tiny Pictures from Japan

The writing of haiku, *strictly patterned, three-lined poems, is one of the traditional arts of Japan. Most* haiku *suggest a mood, or feeling, by painting tiny,* clear-cut *pictures. Because the poems are very short, the poet can include only the most important details of his scene.*

POPPIES

Unknown

❧

O winds of Heaven, pray,
A moment calm your tumult,
For the poppies bloom today.

FOXES PLAYING

Buson TRANSLATED BY WILLIAM N. PORTER

❧

The moon is shining bright,
And 'round my white narcissus beds
The foxes play all night.

THE HERON

Zuiryu

❧

The floating heron
Pecks at it till it shatters—
Full-moon-on-water.

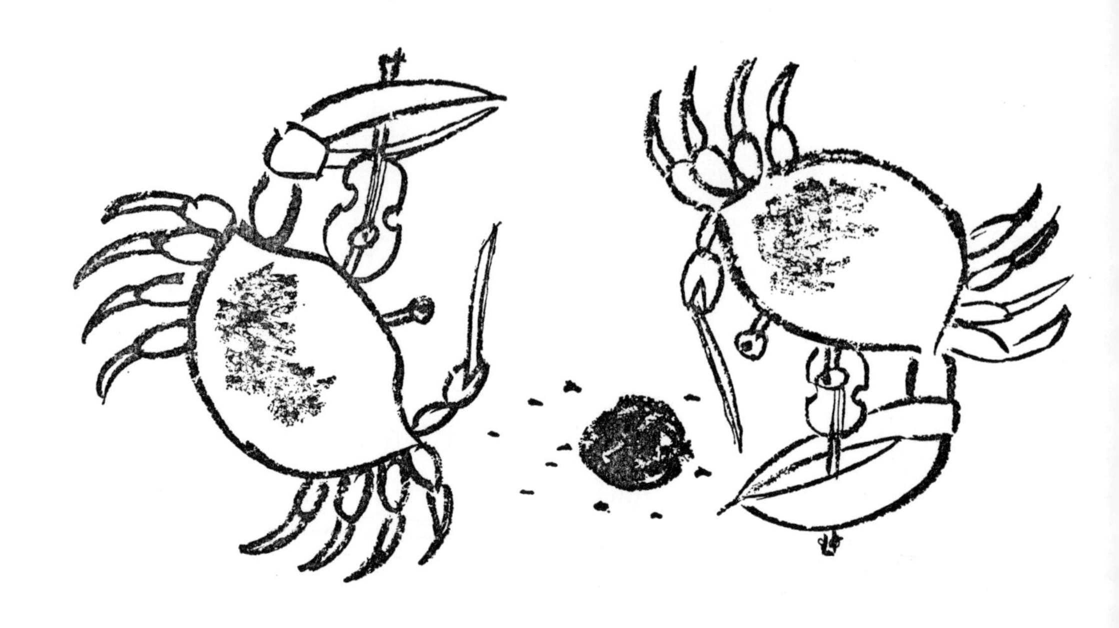

FIDDLER CRABS

Madeline Howard, age 10

Their eyes on thin stalks
Peer and glare at everything.
They live in small holes.

THE WORLD UPSIDE DOWN

Onitsura TRANSLATED BY HAROLD G. HENDERSON

A trout leaps high—
Below him, in the river bottom,
Clouds flow by.

ON THE ROAD TO NARA

Basho TRANSLATED BY HAROLD G. HENDERSON

Oh, these spring days!
A nameless little mountain,
Wrapped in morning haze!

CATTLE

Banko TRANSLATED BY WILLIAM N. PORTER

How cool the cattle seem!
They love to swish their tails and stand
Knee-deep within the stream.

THE CAT

Issa TRANSLATED BY HAROLD G. HENDERSON

Sleeping, then waking
and giving a great yawn, the cat
goes out love-making.

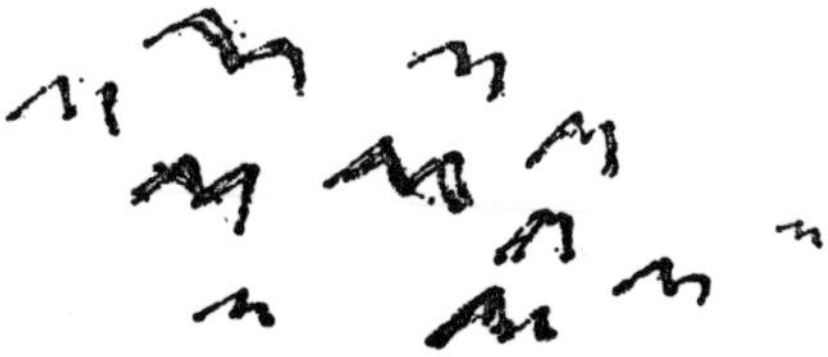

THE BARLEY FIELD

Sora TRANSLATED BY HAROLD G. HENDERSON

Up the barley rows,
Stitching, stitching them together,
A butterfly goes.

IN THE PADDY FIELD

Raizan TRANSLATED BY HAROLD G. HENDERSON

Women, rice-planting:
All muddy, save for one thing—
That's their chanting.

SUMMER WIND

Barbara Johnson, age 13

❦

Breath of a dragon,
Whispering round my window—
The soft summer wind.

COOLNESS

Onitsura TRANSLATED BY HAROLD G. HENDERSON

❦

How cool the breeze:
The sky is filled with voices—
Pine and cedar trees.

BABY'S HANDS

Gomei TRANSLATED BY WILLIAM N. PORTER

❧

One chestnut, only one,
Is all his tiny hands can hold,
My little baby son.

THE LITTLE VALLEY IN SPRING

Onitsura TRANSLATED BY HAROLD G. HENDERSON

❧

A mountain stream:
Even the stones make songs—
Wild cherry trees.

SPRING RAINS

Buson TRANSLATED BY HAROLD G. HENDERSON

❧

As the spring rains fall,
Soaking in them, on the roof,
Is a child's rag ball.

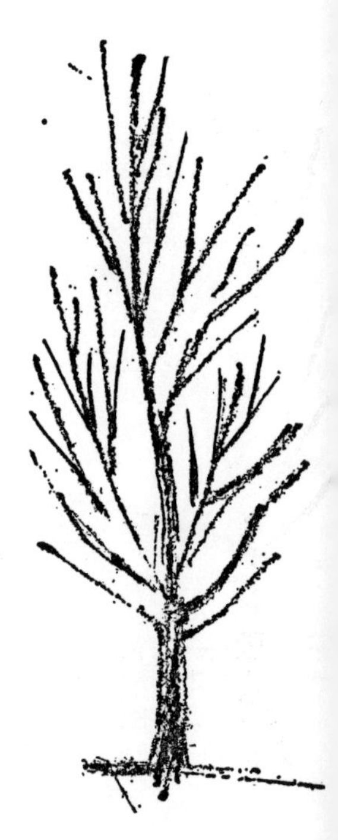

THE GOOD NEIGHBOR

Koyo

Night, and the moon!
My neighbor, playing on his flute—
Out of tune!

MY HUT

Issa

In winter moonlight
A clear look at my old hut—
Dilapidated.

WILD GEESE

Roka

❧

Now wild geese return—
What draws them crying, crying
All the long dark night?

ONITSURA'S FIRST POEM

Onitsura, age 8 TRANSLATED BY HAROLD G. HENDERSON

❧

Although I say,
"Come here! Come here!" the fireflies
Keep flying away!

VALENTINE GREETINGS

Kathyrn Sexton, age 14

❧

Gold dust in the sky,
Lacy clouds that dip about—
Nature's valentine.

THE SPARROW

Shiki

Good morning, sparrow—
Writing on my clean veranda
With your dewy feet.

FROGS

Wakyu

Squads of frogs jumped in
When they heard the plunk-plash
Of a single frog.

THE END OF SUMMER

Basho TRANSLATED BY HAROLD G. HENDERSON

❧

The beginning of fall:
  The ocean, the rice fields—
    One green for all!

MY LITTLE SWORD-BEARER

Shigen TRANSLATED BY WILLIAM N. PORTER

❧

Where is the boy? Hallo!
  The little lad who bears my sword
    Has tumbled in the snow!

HAIKU

Roger Pearson, grade 6

❧

Is it a flower,
  Or is it just a bit of
    Paint, or a white moth?

MOUNT FUJI

Onitsura TRANSLATED BY OLIVE BEAUPRÉ MILLER

Around a turn, and suddenly
There against the autumn skies,
Behold the mighty Fuji rise!

HAIKU

Deborah Basnett, grade 7

The eye of the rain
Very high on the mountain
Is looking for you.

HAIKU

Debby Innes

In all this wide world
People are like the locusts
Swarming in the field.

HAIKU

Devra Jeffers, grade 7

Flowers are fragile
And like the soft, soft velvet
Of a horse's nose.

III

Maxims and Proverbs

Little verses called "maxims" or "proverbs," were once used to teach children great truths and proper behavior. Some of these that follow are very old, others are by modern poets.

OLD NEW ENGLAND MAXIM

Unknown

❧

Use it up,
  Wear it out;
Make it do,
  Or do without.

SHADOWS *(Written more than two hundred years ago)*

Anna E. Hamilton

❧

This learned I from the shadow of a tree
That to and fro did sway against a wall—
Our shadow selves, our influence may fall
Where we ourselves can never be.

This poem was found on an old sundial in Germany.

LESSON FROM A SUNDIAL

❧

Ignore dull days; forget the showers;
Keep count of only shining hours.

BE LIKE THE BIRD

Victor Hugo

Be like the bird, who
Halting in his flight
On limb too slight
Feels it give way beneath him,
Yet sings
Knowing he hath wings.

PRIMER LESSON

Carl Sandburg

❦

Look out how you use proud words.
When you let proud words go, it is not
  easy to call them back.
They wear long boots, hard boots;
  they walk off proud; they can't
  hear you calling—
Look out how you use proud words.

OF COURTESY

Arthur Guiterman

❦

Good manners may in Seven Words be found:
Forget Yourself and think of Those Around.

DUTY

Edwin Markham

❦

When Duty comes a-knocking at your gate,
Welcome him in; for if you bid him wait,
He will depart only to come once more
And bring seven other duties to your door.

OF QUARRELS

Arthur Guiterman

No Quarrel ever Stirred
Before the Second Word.

HURT NO LIVING THING

Christina Rossetti

Hurt no living thing:
Ladybird nor butterfly,
Nor moth with dusty wing,
Nor cricket chirping cheerily,
Nor grasshopper so light of leap,
Nor dancing gnat, nor beetle fat,
Nor harmless worms that creep.

Some of America's most famous proverbs come from Poor Richard's Almanac, *by Benjamin Franklin. Here are two of the best known.*

Little strokes
Fell great oaks.

Well begun
Is half done.

FOR EVERY EVIL UNDER THE SUN

Mother Goose

For every evil under the sun
There is a cure, or there is none.
If there is one, try and find it;
If there be none, never mind it.

IV

Emotion

Many poems express pure feeling: joy, sorrow,
longing, excitement—
Can you name some of the emotions these poems put into words?

ARIEL'S SONG

William Shakespeare

Where the bee sucks, there suck I:
In a cowslip's bell I lie;
There I couch when owls do cry.
On the bat's back I do fly
After summer merrily.
Merrily, merrily shall I live now
Under the blossom that hangs on the bough.

GLADDE THINGS

Unknown English poet of several hundred years ago.

Of gladde things there be four, ay four:
A Larke above ye olde nest blithely singing,
A wild Rose clinging
In safety to a rock, a Shepherd bringing
A Lambe found in his arms,
And Christmasse Bells a-ringing.

INVITATION

Ridgely Torrence

❧

Let's play we are a tune
And make a kind of song
About the sun and moon
Before the stars were born.
You be the breath, I'll be the horn,
It will not take us long.

VAGABONDIA

Gertrude Buckman, high school

Roads that are straight
And that end at a gate
Are not half so enticing to follow
As are long roads that twist
And are lost in the mist
Like the path of the South-flying swallow.

CONSCIENCE

Issa TRANSLATED BY HAROLD G. HENDERSON

Somehow it seems wrong:
To take one's noonday nap and hear
A rice-planting song.

A LOVER TO HIS DOUBTING LADY

J.J.

❧

Who?
You!

SONG

Hilda Conkling, age 5

❧

I will sing you a song,
Sweets of my heart,
With love in it,
(How I love you!)
And a rose to swing in the wind,
The wind that swings roses!

CLËIS

Sappho TRANSLATED BY J. M. EDMONDS

❧

I have a little daughter rare
That's like the golden flowers fair,
        My Clëis;
I would not take all Lydia wide,
No, nor lovely Greece beside
        For Clëis.

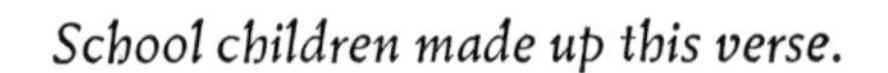

School children made up this verse.

MY LOVE FOR YOU

I love you little, I love you lots;
My love for you would fill ten pots,
Fifteen buckets, sixteen cans,
Three teacups and four dishpans.

SINGING-TIME

Rose Fyleman

I wake in the morning early
And always, the very first thing,
I poke out my head and I sit up in bed
And I sing and I sing and I sing.

The poetess of Ancient Greece writes of a young girl experiencing the first pangs of love:

MOTHER, I CANNOT MIND MY WHEEL

Sappho TRANSLATED BY WALTER SAVAGE LANDOR

Mother, I cannot mind my wheel;
  My fingers ache, my lips are dry;
Oh! if you felt the pain I feel!
  But oh, who ever felt as I!

And a modern student poet treats the experience of first love:

LOVE

Frederico Velasquez, age 15

How much do I love you?
I cannot say.
Why, why is it,
When I see you coming,
I turn and go the other way?

TO MY VALENTINE

Unknown

If apples were pears,
And peaches were plums,
And the rose had a different name;
If tigers were bears,
And fingers were thumbs,
I'd love you just the same!

The buffaloes in the following poem are not just animals, they represent part of American history.

BUFFALO DUSK

Carl Sandburg

The buffaloes are gone.
And those who saw the buffaloes are gone.
Those who saw the buffaloes by thousands and
  how they pawed the prairie sod into dust
  with their hoofs, their great heads down
  pawing on in a great pageant of dusk,
Those who saw the buffaloes are gone.
And the buffaloes are gone.

MY MAID MARY

Unknown

My maid Mary she minds the dairy,
While I go a-hoeing and a-mowing each morn;
Gaily run the reel and the little spinning wheel,
Whilst I am singing and mowing my corn.

A MEMORY

William Allingham

Four ducks on a pond,
A grass bank beyond,
A blue sky of spring,
White clouds on the wing;
What a little thing
To remember for years—
To remember with tears!

MULTIPLICATION

Unknown

Multiplication is vexation,
Division is as bad;
The Rule of Three doth puzzle me,
And Practice drives me mad.

This song was part of a play presented in England in 1612.

SONG FOR A DANCE

Francis Beaumont

Shake off your heavy trance!
And leap into a dance
Such as no mortal use to tread:
Fit only for Apollo
To play to, for the moon to lead,
And all the stars to follow.

AFRICAN LULLABY

Unknown East African poet

Sleep, sleep, my little one! The night is all wind and rain;
The meal has been wet by the raindrops
and bent is the sugar cane;
O Giver who gives to the people, in safety my little son keep!
My little son with the headdress, sleep, sleep, sleep!

LOST

A prairie child, late nineteenth century.

Big prairie,
Little me.

The deepest emotions are often expressed in the simplest words. In a poem entitled "Lucy," the great English poet William Wordsworth could find only this to say of the death of a young girl:

". . . she is in her grave, and, oh
The difference to me!"

Can you feel the emotion he could not fully express?

Long before Wordsworth lived, the great Japanese haiku *poet Basho visited the garden where as a child, he had played and studied with his first and dearest friend. The friend had since died and Basho mourned him deeply. This is how he expressed the greatest sorrow of his life.*

CHERRY BLOSSOMS

Basho TRANSLATED BY HAROLD G. HENDERSON

Many, many things
they bring to mind—
cherry blossoms!

Two thousand years ago in Greece some boys mourned a dog who died.

THE MALTESE DOG

Tymnes TRANSLATED BY EDMUND BLUNDEN

He came from Malta; and Eumelus says
He had no better dog in all his days.
We called him Bull; he went into the dark,
Along those roads we cannot hear him bark.

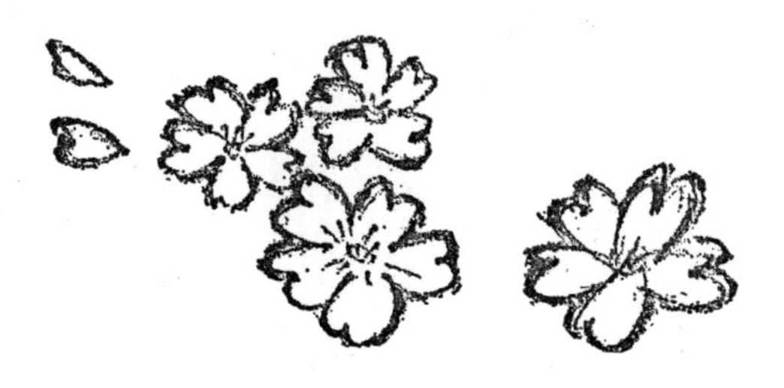

V

Riddle Songs

Riddle songs are very old and are still written today. Why not try writing some yourself?

THE YEAR

Unknown

There is a tree of praise and dower
That beareth much of fruit and flower;
Twelve branches has it, spreading wide,
Where two-and-fifty nests abide,
In every nest the birds are seven:
Thankèd be the King of heaven.

A RIDDLE

Christina Rossetti

There is one that has a head without an eye,
   And there's one that has an eye without a head:
You may find the answer if you try;
   And when all is said,
Half the answer hangs upon a thread.

AS I WAS GOING TO SAINT IVES

Unknown

As I was going to Saint Ives,
I met a man with seven wives,
Each wife had seven sacks,
Each sack had seven cats,
Each cat had seven kits:
Kits, cats, sacks, and wives,
How many were there going to Saint Ives?

A SUM

Lewis Carroll

I give thee all, I can no more,
   Though small thy share may be:
Two halves, three thirds, and quarters four
   Is all I bring to thee.

VI

Laughter

Not only does poetry give us pleasure by letting us see something familiar in a new way, but it can also give us a less quiet happiness by making us laugh.

BOUGHT LOCKS

Marcus Valerius Martialis

TRANSLATED BY SIR JOHN HARRINGTON

❧

The golden hair that Gulla wears
  Is hers: who would have thought it?
She swears 'tis hers, and true she swears,
  For I know where she bought it.

BARBER, BARBER

Mother Goose

❧

Barber, barber, shave a pig,
How many hairs will make a wig?
"Four-and-twenty, that's enough."
Give the barber a pinch of snuff.

THE BOY

Lisa Gorton, grade 2

❧

I know a boy.
He went to the store
And he came back
With an apple core.

THE PURPLE COW

Gelett Burgess

I never saw a Purple Cow,
  I never hope to see one;
But I can tell you, anyhow,
  I'd rather see than be one!

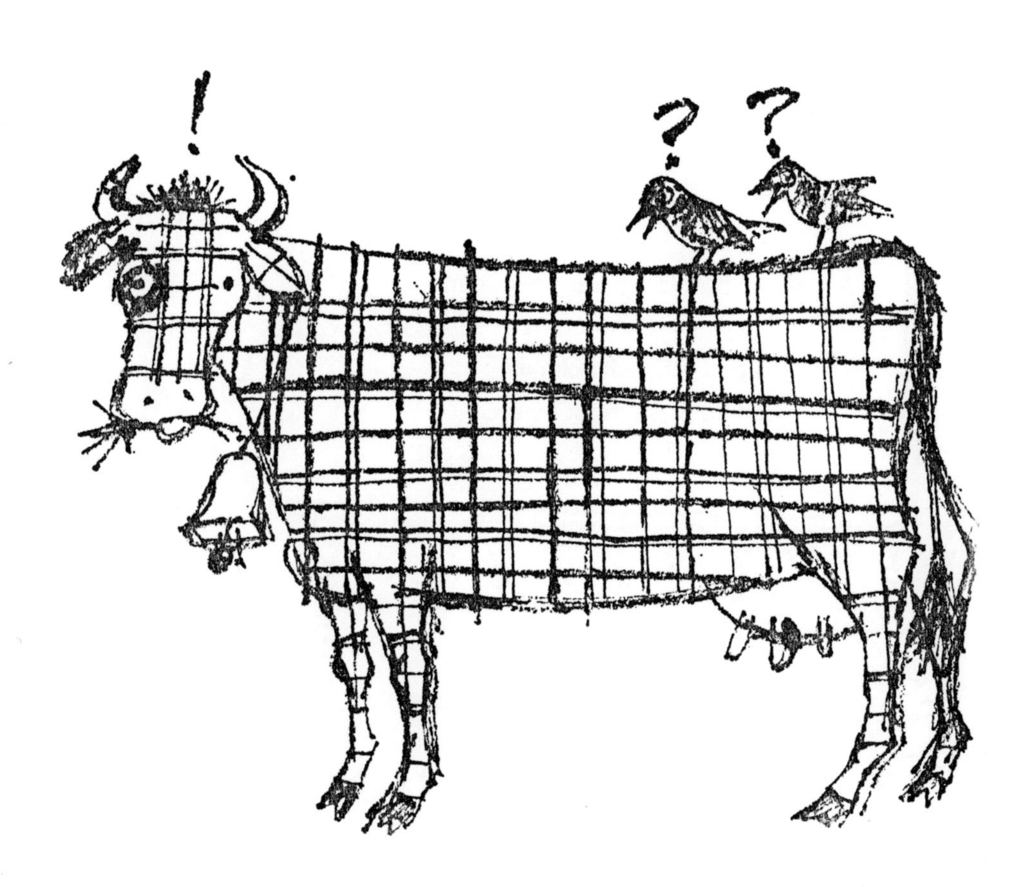

NIKON'S NOSE

Nicarchus

What's come? The end of Nikon's nose,
    But him I cannot see!
Run up the hill, and I suppose
In the far distance Nikon shows—
    He'll be here presently!

THE ELEPHANT

Hilaire Belloc

When people call this beast to mind,
    They marvel more and more
At such a *little* tail behind,
    So LARGE a trunk before.

According to the newspaper columnist, Don Marquis, this poem was one of many written by Archy the Cockroach, who took over the newspaperman's typewriter at night. Archy could not manage the keys which make capital letters and punctuation.

THE HONEY BEE

Don Marquis

the honey bee is sad and cross
and wicked as a weasel
and when she perches on you boss
she leaves a little measle

Part of the fun in this poem is that the poet, reflecting his confusion about the octopus, mixes high-blown "poetic" language with bad grammar.

THE OCTOPUS

Ogden Nash

Tell me, O Octopus, I begs,
Is those things arms, or is they legs?
I marvel at thee, Octopus!
If I were Thou, I'd call me us.

LITANY FOR HALLOWEEN

Unknown. From Scotland.

From Ghoulies and Ghosties,
Long-leggety Beasties,
And THINGS
That go BUMP in the night,
Good Lord, deliver us!

THE CAMEL

Ogden Nash

The camel has a single hump;
The dromedary, two;
Or else the other way around.
I'm never sure. Are you?

THE MULE

Unknown

On a mule you find two feet behind,
Two feet you find before;
You stand behind before you find
What the two behind be for.

School children told these to each other for several generations. They probably made them up, too.

I'VE GOT A DOG

Unknown

I've got a dog as thin as a rail,
He's got fleas all over his tail;
Every time his tail goes flop,
The fleas on the bottom all hop to the top.

AN EPICURE

Unknown

An epicure, dining at Crewe,
Found quite a large mouse in his stew.
Said the waiter, "Don't shout,
And wave it about,
Or the rest will be wanting one too!"

AN OLD MAN FROM PERU

Unknown

There was an old man from Peru
Who dreamed he was eating his shoe;
He woke in a fright
In the middle of the night
And found it was perfectly true.

I EAT MY PEAS WITH HONEY

American. Unknown.

I eat my peas with honey,
I've done it all my life,
It makes the peas taste funny,
But it keeps them on my knife.

Another form of nonsense poem is called a limerick.
A hundred years ago or so, Edward Lear wrote a book of funny limericks. This form of verse has been popular ever since.
Can you find the pattern of rhyme and try some of your own?

OLD MAN WITH A BEARD

Edward Lear

There was an Old Man with a beard
Who said, "It is just as I feared!
  Two Owls and a Hen,
  Four Larks and a Wren,
Have all built their nests in my beard!"

A FLEA AND A FLY

Unknown

A flea and a fly in a flue
Were imprisoned, so what could they do?
Said the fly, "Let us flee,"
Said the flea, "Let us fly,"
So they flew through a flaw in the flue.

ON DIGITAL EXTREMITIES

Gelett Burgess

I'd rather have fingers than toes;
I'd rather have eyes than a nose;
And as for my hair,
I'm glad it's all there;
I'll be awfully sad when it goes!

I WISH THAT MY ROOM HAD A FLOOR

Gelett Burgess

❧

I wish that my room had a floor;
I don't so much care for a door,
 But this walking around
 Without touching the ground
Is getting to be quite a bore.

THE TUTOR

Carolyn Wells

❧

A tutor who tooted the flute
Tried to tutor two tooters to toot.
 Said the two to the tutor,
 "Is it harder to toot or
To tutor two tooters to toot?"

THE MAN IN THE WILDERNESS

Mother Goose

The man in the wilderness asked me,
How many strawberries grew in the sea.
I answered him, as I thought good,
As many red herrings as grew in the wood.

THE YOUNG LADY OF NIGER

Unknown

There was a young lady of Niger
Who smiled as she rode on a tiger;
They returned from the ride
With the lady inside,
And the smile on the face of the tiger.

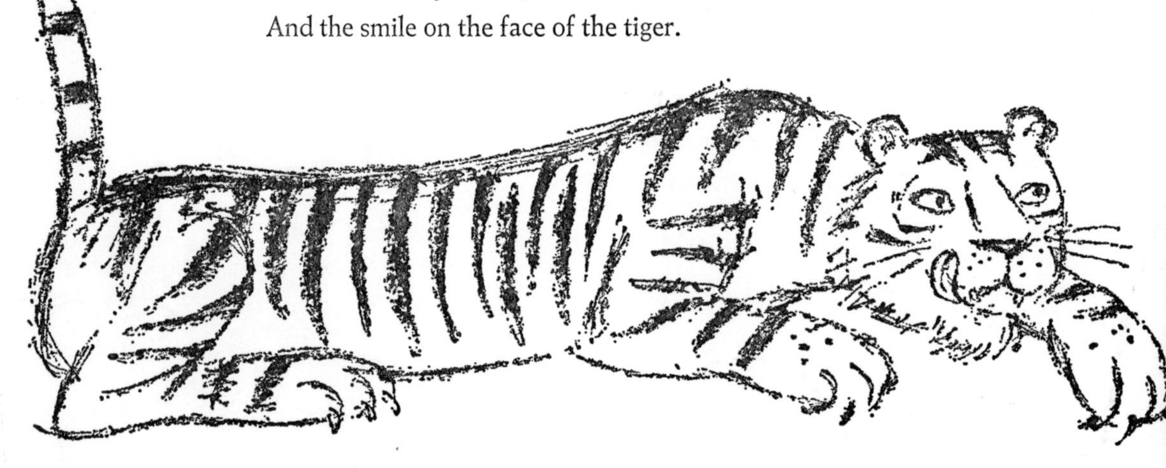

An epitaph is a short statement written in memory of someone who has died. Most epitaphs are serious, but here are some amusing ones written years ago.

From an old ENGLISH GRAVEYARD

A zealous Locke-Smith Dyed of late
And did arrive at heaven gate,
He stood without and would not knocke
Because he meant to picke the locke.

From a NEW YORK STATE CEMETERY

This is my obituary:
I ran my farm, and I ran my dairy.
I would have had a longer life
If ever I'd learned to run my wife.

From NEW ENGLAND

This is the grave of Mike O'Day
Who died maintaining his right of way.
His right was clear, his will was strong,
But he's just as dead as if he'd been wrong.

EPITAPH FOR CHARLES II OF ENGLAND

John Wilmot, Earl of Rochester

Here lies a good and mighty King,
   Whose Promise none relys on;
He never said a Foolish thing
   Nor ever did a Wise one.

From a NEW ENGLAND GRAVEYARD

Beneath this stone, a lump of clay,
   Lies Uncle Peter Daniels
Who too early on the month of May
   Took off his winter flannels

From an OHIO GRAVEYARD

Here lies a man
Of great intelligence.
He knew what he ought to do,
But never did Commence.

VII

People

These verses are about human beings with all the strengths, weaknesses, joys, and sorrows we share in common.

THE KING OF FRANCE

Mother Goose

The King of France went up the hill
With twenty thousand men;
The King of France came down the hill,
And ne'er went up again.

MEXICAN MARKET WOMAN

Langston Hughes

This ancient hag
Who sits upon the ground
Selling her scanty wares
Day in, day round,
Has known high wind-swept mountains,
And the sun has made
Her skin so brown.

THE RAG PICKER

Ransetsu TRANSLATED BY OLIVE BEAUPRÉ MILLER

Through winter's first cold snow,
See the poor shivering rag-man go,—
Yet he, too, is a son of man.

THE TRADESMAN

Unknown

If I were a tailor, I'd make it my boast
The best of all tailors to be.
If I were a tinker, no tinker beside
Should mend an old kettle like me.

THE HUNTER

Ogden Nash

The hunter crouches in his blind
'Neath camouflage of every kind,
And conjures up a quacking noise
To lend allure to his decoys.
This grown-up man, with pluck and luck,
Is hoping to outwit a duck.

IANTHE

Walter Savage Landor

❧

From you, Ianthe, little troubles pass
   Like little ripples down a sunny river;
Your pleasures spring like daisies in the grass,
   Cut down and up again as blithe as ever.

In this poem, the poet imagines what the neighbors may have said when Abraham Lincoln was born.

WELL, DID YOU HEAR?

Edmund Vance Cook

❧

Well, did you hear? Tom Lincoln's wife today,
The devil's luck for folks as poor as they!
Poor Tom! Poor Nance!
Poor youngun born without a chance!

THE POET'S SHIELD

Archilochus TRANSLATED BY SIR W. MORRIS

A perfect shield bedecks some Thracian now;
I had no choice: I left it in a wood.
Ah, well, I saved my skin, so let it go!
A new one's just as good.

What does the title add to the meaning of this short poem?

THE SPAN OF LIFE

Robert Frost

The old dog barks backward without getting up.
I can remember when he was a pup.

Although but one line long, and in free verse, this is still poetry if you can feel its rhythm and grasp its meaning.
(An estuary is the mouth of a river.)

TO OLD AGE

Walt Whitman

I see in you the estuary that enlarges and spreads itself grandly
as it pours in the great sea.

A student poet remarks on the uniqueness of each man.

HAIKU

Dick Sanders, grade 8

Once gone from the earth
There is no substitution.
None can take your place.

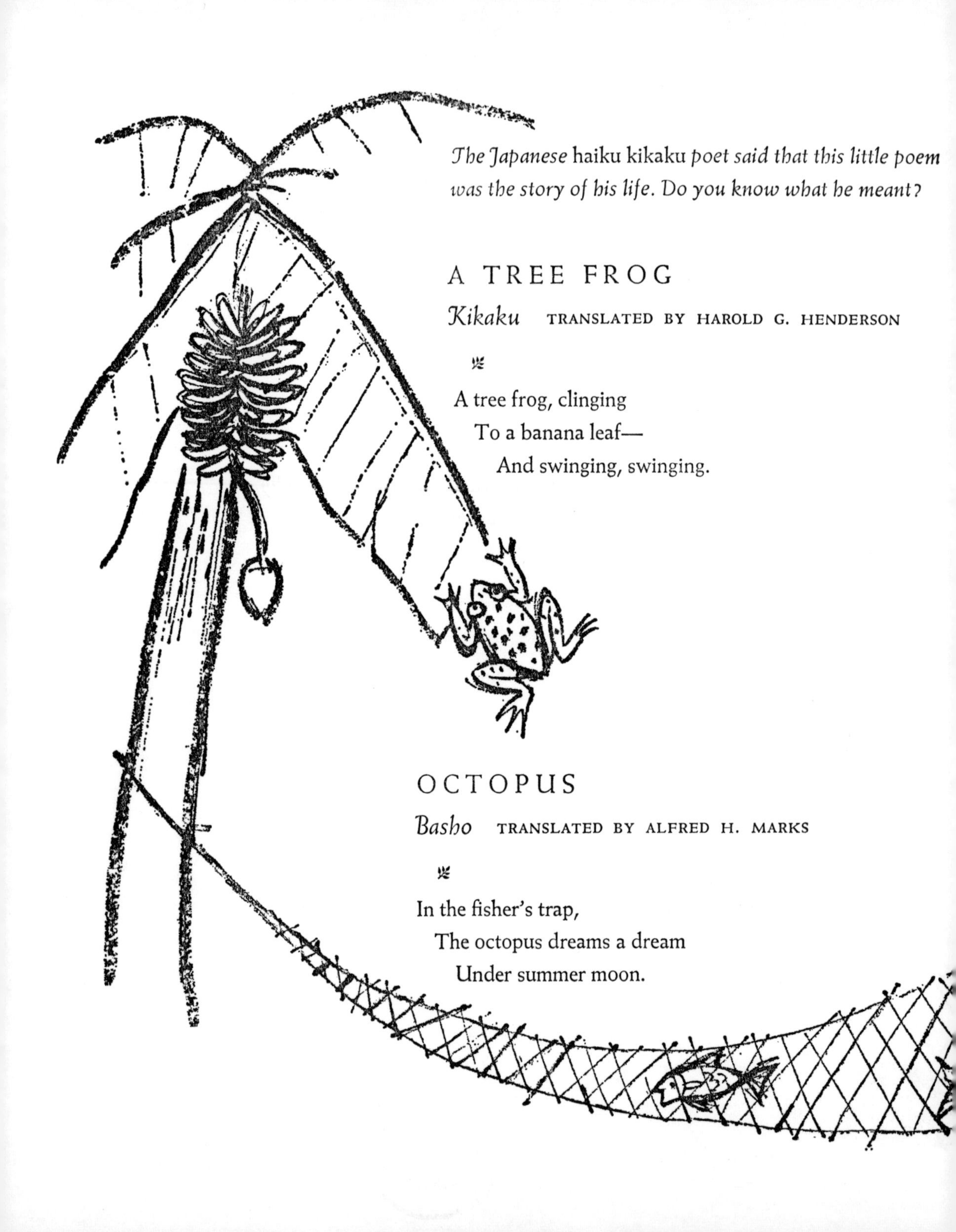

The Japanese haiku kikaku *poet said that this little poem was the story of his life. Do you know what he meant?*

A TREE FROG

Kikaku TRANSLATED BY HAROLD G. HENDERSON

A tree frog, clinging
To a banana leaf—
And swinging, swinging.

OCTOPUS

Basho TRANSLATED BY ALFRED H. MARKS

In the fisher's trap,
The octopus dreams a dream
Under summer moon.

This is a poem about a dandelion, but it is also about a kind of person. Do you know anyone who resembles this dandelion?

DANDELION

Hilda Conkling, age 9

O little soldier with the golden helmet,
What are you guarding on my lawn?
You with your green gun
And your yellow beard,
Why do you stand so stiff?
There is only the grass to fight!

OLD STONES

Elizabeth Coatsworth

Stones have a dull peace of their own.
I sometimes wish that I were a stone.
What helps to make them look secure
is being rounded, to be sure.
Young stones have edges like a thorn,
but old stones are serene and worn.

TOMMY TROT

Mother Goose

Tommy Trot, a man of law,
Sold his bed and lay upon straw;
Sold the straw and slept on grass,
To buy his wife a looking-glass.

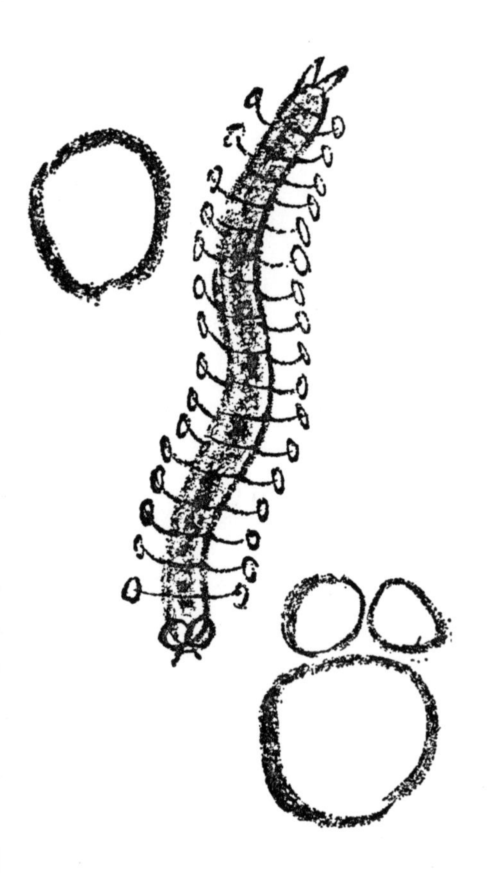

THE PUZZLED CENTIPEDE

Unknown

A centipede was happy quite,
Until a frog in fun
Said, "Pray, which leg comes after which?"
This raised her mind to such a pitch,
She lay distracted in the ditch
Considering how to run.

A WEE LITTLE WORM

James Whitcomb Riley

A wee little worm in a hickory-nut
   Sang, happy as he could be,
"O I live in the heart of the whole round world,
   And it all belongs to me!"

THE OPTIMIST

Unknown

The optimist fell ten stories,
   And at each window bar
He shouted to the folks inside:
   "Doing all right so far!"

LOOKING FORWARD

Robert Louis Stevenson

When I am grown to man's estate
I shall be very proud and great,
And tell the other girls and boys
Not to meddle with my toys.

THE HARDSHIP OF ACCOUNTING

Robert Frost

Never ask of money spent
Where the spender thinks it went
Nobody was ever meant
To remember or invent
What he did with every cent.

A COW AT SULLINGTON

Charles Dalmon

She leaves the puddle where she drinks,
  And comes toward the roadway bar
And looks into our eyes, and thinks
  What curious creatures we are!

VIII

Wisdom

Probably the finest poets are those who are not only poets, but also philosophers. In the poems that follow, the writers look at familiar things and in them find meanings that help us to understand life better.

As you read each poem, try to understand what the writer is saying to you.

STANDARDS

Charles Wharton Stork

White is the skimming gull on the somber green of the firtrees,
Black is the soaring gull on a snowy glimmer of cloud.

FLOWER IN THE CRANNIED WALL

Alfred, Lord Tennyson

Flower in the crannied wall,
I pluck you out of the crannies,
I hold you here, root and all, in my hand,
Little flower—but *if* I could understand
What you are, root and all, and all in all,
I should know what God and man is.

SPLINTER

Carl Sandburg

The voice of the last cricket
across the first frost
is one kind of good-by.
It is so thin a splinter of singing.

PEDIGREE

Emily Dickinson

The pedigree of honey
Does not concern the bee;
A clover, any time, to him
Is aristocracy.

TO MAKE A PRAIRIE

Emily Dickinson

To make a prairie it takes a clover
    and one bee—
One clover, and a bee,
And revery.
The revery alone will do
If bees are few.

What is the kite's soul? What does this poem tell us of human experience?

THE KITE

Kubonta

Fallen now to earth
After dancing journeyings—
Kite that lost its soul.

ON SEEING WEATHERBEATEN TREES

Adelaide Crapsey

Is it as plainly in our living shown,
By slant and twist, which way the wind hath blown?

LINES ON THE ANTIQUITY OF MICROBES

Strickland Gillilan

❧

Adam
Had 'em.

THE PARASOL

Seiho

TRANSLATED BY HAROLD G. HENDERSON

❧

Dear, your parasol,
In all this blazing sunshine—
Is so very small!

SOUNDS

Wafu TRANSLATED BY HAROLD G. HENDERSON

❧

Insects one hears—
And one hears the talk of men—
With different ears.

ICICLES

Onitsura

As to icicles
  I often wonder why they grow
    Some long—some short.

THE FIRST FIREFLY

Issa

The first firefly . . .
  But he got away and I . . .
    Air in my fingers.

LODGED

Robert Frost

The rain to the wind said
"You push and I'll pelt."
They so smote the garden bed
That the flowers actually knelt,
And lay lodged—though not dead.

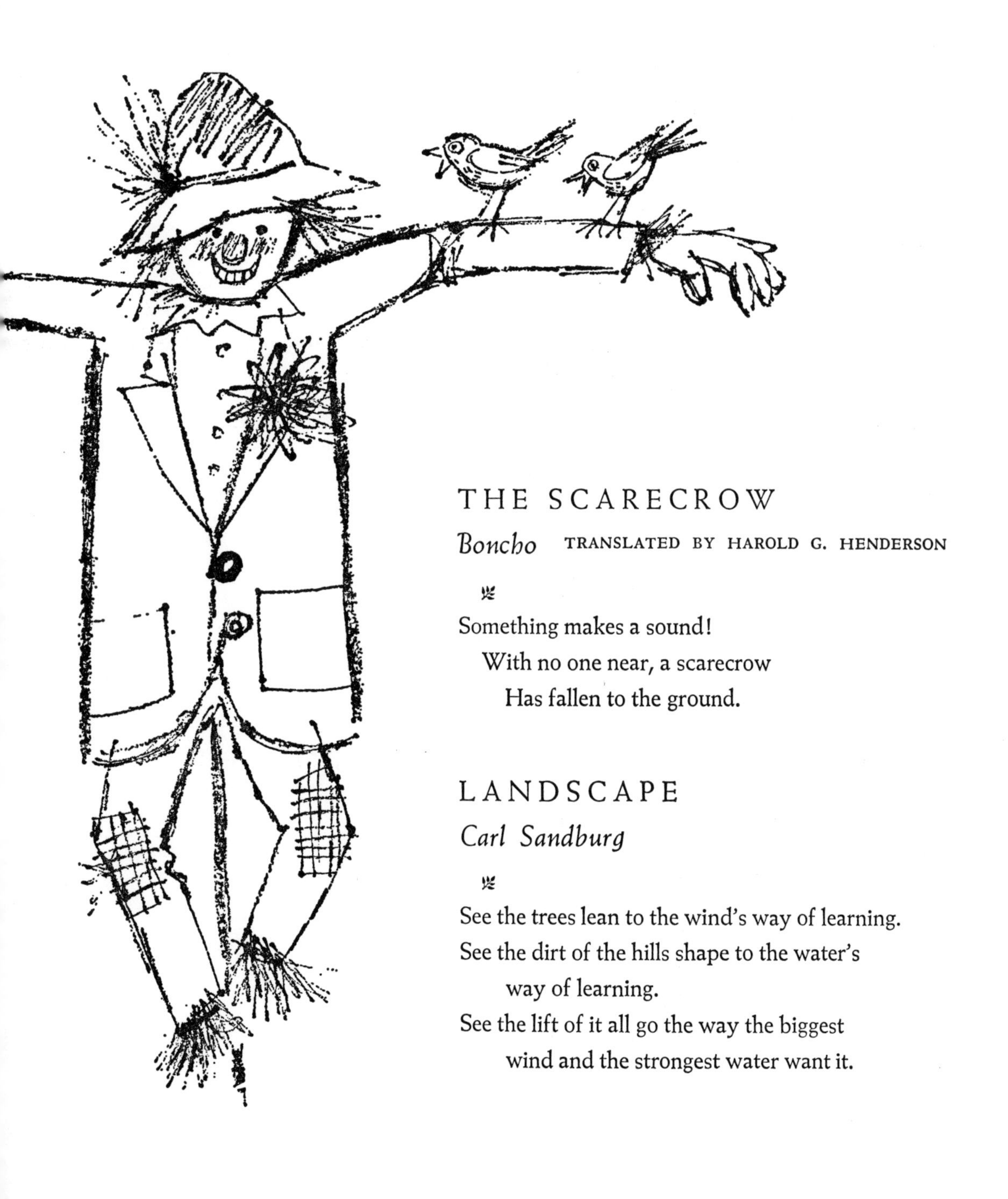

THE SCARECROW

Boncho TRANSLATED BY HAROLD G. HENDERSON

Something makes a sound!
With no one near, a scarecrow
Has fallen to the ground.

LANDSCAPE

Carl Sandburg

See the trees lean to the wind's way of learning.
See the dirt of the hills shape to the water's
way of learning.
See the lift of it all go the way the biggest
wind and the strongest water want it.

GRASSROOTS

Carl Sandburg

Grass clutches at the dark dirt with finger holds.
Let it be blue grass, barley, rye or wheat,
Let it be button weed or butter-and-eggs,
Let it be Johnny-jumpups springing clean blue streaks.
Grassroots down under put fingers into dark dirt.

LIGHTNING

Japanese TRANSLATED BY OLIVE BEAUPRÉ MILLER

A flash of lightning bright!
  Then darker, darker than before
    The blackness of the night!

FIREFLIES IN THE GARDEN

Robert Frost

Here come real stars to fill the upper skies,
And here on earth come emulating flies,
That though they never equal stars in size,
(And they were never really stars at heart)
Achieve at times a very star-like start.
Only, of course, they can't sustain the part.

THE SUN

Jodelle Hulse, grade 7

❧

The sun
Is like a big
Golden eye in the sky.
This mammoth eye, guarding the earth
Is life.

PHILOSOPHICAL POEM

Unknown

❧

I?
Why?

And just because this is what is called a "universal" (common to all people) question, we repeat it in

French

Moi?
Pourquoi?

Spanish

¿Yo?
¿Porqué?

And German.

Ich?
Warum?

Writing Poetry

IMAGES

Above all, writing poetry demands sharp senses and an active imagination. The poet looks, listens, smells, touches, and tastes. He discovers that some things remind him of other things. He compares one thing to another. He puts this comparison into words, and it is called an image. *Here are some images from the poems in this book:*

the ashes . . . seem like a million unlit stars ("A Fire")
the sun is like a big golden eye in the sky ("The Sun")
the rabbits . . . blown through the silver hollow . . .
like puffs of snow ("White Season")

Sometimes the comparisons are more direct:
the heavenly washing is hung out to dry ("Washerwoman's Song")
the banners of the corn ("Cricket March")
the children scuffle through fallen gold ("Blue Smoke")

Sometimes an object or idea seems to have human qualities:
I have seen Spring lift her head ("Robin's Song")
grass clutches at the dark dirt with finger holds ("Grassroots")
when Duty comes a-knocking at your gate ("Duty")

And sometimes the whole poem is a single comparison:
"Summer Wind," "Icebergs," "Mountains," "Popcorn," "On Seeing Weatherbeaten Trees," "The Barley Field."

What is the comparison in each poem?

For practice, you might pick out the most impressive sights, sounds, and other sensations of each day, and try to put them into words. Of what do they remind you? The more unexpected and original a comparison, the more effective it usually is.

Next, you will want to put your thoughts and images into some kind of pattern.

PATTERNS

Verse is the arrangement of words in formal patterns. Many such patterns exist, but there are three that are especially popular with student poets. These patterns are free verse, short rhyming patterns such as couplets and quatrains, and Japanese syllable patterns.

FREE VERSE

You will find an explanation of free verse on page 7. Many fine poems have been written in this form. Some that appear in this book are "Clouds," "Water," "Sea Wash," "The Ship Starting," "Traders," "Grassroots," "Mountains," "Pods," "Cricket March," "Splinter," "December," "Spring," "Dandelion," and "A Fire."

COUPLETS

A couplet has two lines that usually rhyme and contain the same number of syllables. Some of the couplets in this book are "The Span of Life," "Golden Fish," and "On Seeing Weatherbeaten Trees."

Sometimes a poem is made up of two or more couplets. Read the poems called "Old Stones," "Night by the Fire," and "The Breeze" for examples of this form.

QUATRAINS (from the French word *quatre*, meaning four)

A quatrain has four lines, and there are several ways to rhyme them. Study the rhyming patterns of "A Cow at Sullington," "The

Breeze," "Rain," "Blow the Stars Home," "Popcorn," and "Surgeon's Hands."

HAIKU

It is very difficult to translate haiku *poetry into English because the Japanese language is so very different from our own. For example, the Japanese language lacks the strongly accented words we have in English. This makes a difference in the rhythmic patterns of the two languages. For another thing, all Japanese words end in either a vowel or in "n." It would be difficult to rhyme such words without becoming monotonous.* Haiku *poems, therefore, do not rhyme in their original versions, though many translators have rhymed them in English. The verse pattern of a* haiku *poem is actually a pattern of syllables—a five-syllable line, then a seven-syllable line, then another five-syllable line.*

TANKA

The tanka *is a slightly longer Japanese poem that is also patterned in syllables—five syllables in the first and third lines, seven in the second, fourth, and fifth lines.*

CINQUAIN

The cinquain was invented by an American poet, Adelaide Crapsey, who had studied Japanese poetry. It has five lines of two, four, six, eight, then two syllables. Some of the cinquains in this book are "Icebergs," "The Grand Canyon," and "The Sun."

OTHER PATTERNS

There are many other verse patterns that you can learn from reading books about poetry or, better still, from studying poetry itself. Never hesitate to practice writing verse by imitating the poems written by other poets. You will soon find your own voice. Remember that your thoughts and images are most important, your verse pattern is only a container to hold them.

Notes on Some of the Authors

ANYTE. Poet of ancient Greece.

ARCHILOCHUS (seventh century B.C.) Greek lyric poet and writer of satirical verse.

BANKO (1726-99). Japanese *haiku* poet.

BASHO, MATSUO (1644-94). Japanese poet. Called the "father of *haiku*." Perfected the three-line verse form known as *haiku* and instructed a devoted following of younger followers in its use. Orphaned as a boy, he was adopted by a Japanese noble and grew up as the companion of his benefactor's son.

Beaumont, Francis (1584-1616). English poet and dramatist. Best known for the comedies and tragedies he wrote with John Fletcher.

Belloc, Hilaire (1870-1953). English newspaper and magazine writer. Author of verse, novels, essays, history, and biography.

Burgess, Gelett (1866-1959). Born in Boston, Mass. Popular humorist and illustrator.

Carroll, Lewis (1832-98). Real name, Charles Dodgson. English clergyman, mathematician, and writer. Author of *Alice in Wonderland.*

Crapsey, Adelaide (1878-1914). Born in Ohio. Helped to introduce American readers to Japanese poetry. Invented a verse form—the cinquain—based on the five-line Japanese *tanka.*

Cullen, Countee (1903-46). Born in New York City. One of the first Negro poets to win wide recognition. Published five volumes of verse and one novel.

Dickinson, Emily (1830-86). Born and lived in Amherst, Mass. Nearly all of her poems were published after her death. They reflect a deep sensitivity to and a philosophical acceptance of nature, along with a wry sort of humor.

Frost, Robert (1874-1963). Born in San Francisco, Cal., but made his home in New England, from whose people and countryside he drew inspiration for his poetry. Though today he is considered one of America's finest poets, he first won recognition in England.

Hughes, Langston (1902-). Born in Missouri. Poet, librettist, news correspondent, playwright. 1925, winner of first prize offered to Negro writer by magazine *Opportunity*; 1926, first prize Witter Binner undergraduate poetry contest; 1930, Harmon award for literature; 1954, Ainsfield-Wolfe award for best book on race relations.

HUGO, VICTOR (1802-85). One of France's most famous novelists, playrights, and poets.

ISSA (1762-1826). One of the best-loved of Japanese *haiku* poets. Some critics place his delicate and sensitive poetry next to that of the great Matsuo Basho.

LEAR, EDWARD (1812-88). English landscape painter and poet. Best known today for his nonsense verse.

LI-PO (eighth century). Probably the greatest poet China has produced. Lived part of the time in the emperor's palace, but more frequently wandered around the country in disgrace.

MARKHAM, EDWIN (1852-1940). Born in Oregon. After years of obscurity, he achieved fame with a single poem, "The Man with the Hoe."

MARQUIS, DON (1878-1937). Born in Illinois. Journalist and humorist. Best known for his daily column in the old *New York Sun*, where he introduced the cockroach Archie, and the immortal alley cat Mehitabel.

MARTIALIS, MARCUS VALERIUS (A.D. first century). Latin poet and philosopher.

MOTHER GOOSE. There is no historical proof that Mother Goose ever lived, though a number of towns in the United States claim her as a native daughter. Many of the verses attributed to her are said to have been political in nature, and directed at public figures. For more than a hundred years her name has been attached to collections of anonymous verse and jingles for children.

NASH, OGDEN (1902-   ). Born in Rye, New York. Famous for his highly original humorous verse.

OMAR KHAYYÁM (twelfth century). Persian poet and astronomer. Best known as author of *The Rubáiyát*, a collection of short, philosophical poems.

ONITSURA (1660-1738). Japanese *haiku* poet.

RAIZAN (1653-1716). Japanese *haiku* poet.

RILEY, JAMES WHITCOMB (1849-1916). Born in Indiana, and known as the "Hoosier poet." Wrote humorous verse and dialect poems dealing with the simple life.

ROBERTS, ELIZABETH MADDOX (1886-1941). Born in Kentucky. Her *Time of Man*, a novel about poor Kentucky farmers, won her great critical acclaim.

ROBINSON, EDWIN ARLINGTON (1869-1935). Born in Maine. Published sixteen volumes of poetry and two plays. Is numbered among America's finest poets.

ROETHKE, THEODORE (1908-63). Born in Saginaw, Michigan. 1953, awarded prize of the American Academy of Arts and Letters; 1959, Edna St. Vincent Millay prize for poetry. He was awarded the Pulitzer Prize for poetry in 1953.

ROSSETTI, CHRISTINA (1830-94). Born and lived in London, England, where she and her brother, a painter, played active roles in London's literary and artistic world. Published poems for adults, and one book of poems for children.

SANDBURG, CARL (1878-). Born in Illinois. Poet, biographer, folk song singer. Liked best to write about laboring people—factory workers, farmers, etc. Admired Abraham Lincoln above any other American, and devoted years to writing his biography.

SAPPHO (fifth century B.C.) Greek lyric poetess. Although only fragments of her poetry remain, she is ranked among the greatest of Greek poets.

SHAKESPEARE, WILLIAM (1564-1616). Poet and dramatist, probably the greatest in all of England.

SORA (1648-1710). Japanese *haiku* poet.

SWINBURNE, ALGERNON CHARLES (1837-1909). English poet, dramatist, and essayist.

TENNYSON, ALFRED, LORD (1809-92). English poet. Probably best known in America for his poem "In Memoriam" and his "Morte d'Arthur," a retelling in romantic verse of the story of King Arthur and his Knights of the Round Table. Became poet laureate of England when William Wordsworth died.

TITANOMACHIA. Poet of ancient Greece.

TYMNES. Poet of ancient Greece.

WHITMAN, WALT (1819-92). Born on Long Island, New York. Poet, editor, and journalist. Called himself "the poet of democracy." Claimed to write for the masses, but they did not like his poetry. One of the first truly original American poets.

WILLIAMS, WILLIAM CARLOS (1883-1962). Born in Rutherford, New Jersey, and lived there until his death. Physician and poet. Famous for his epic treatment in verse of the working people among whom he practiced medicine.

Index of Titles

Index of Authors

Index of First Lines